Copyright

Artrezor
All rights reserved.

ISBN: 978-3-9525388-1-4

Cover Photograph
by Fabiola Peñalba / Unsplash

I AM
SUPER FERTILE

COLORING BOOK FOR
WOMEN TRYING TO CONCEIVE

ARTREZOR™

WELCOME

Trying to conceive can be a long and tough journey with its ups and downs. Many women experience excessive stress and frustration during their (trying to conceive) TTC journey.

Our coloring book gives you the opportunity to calm your mind and better focus on your inner goals while motivating yourself - even if you have no one to turn to.

On each coloring page you find a self-motivational quote that can contribute to a better emotional well-being.

This coloring book does not have specific coloring instructions. Bring out the artist in you. Believe in yourself, in your body and prepare your mind for a successful fertility journey.

We wish you wonderful coloring, a balanced mind and all the baby success!

Warmly,

Artrezor

Test Page

Test Page

My dream

Positive energy flows into my womb

My body is able to conceive

My body is
able to carry a
healthy baby to term

I am so happy to
see my little baby bump

Me and my growing baby bump

I am able to give birth to my child

Our child is a gift

Blood flows happily in my body

All is well

We welcome you into our home

At this time angels unite & help

Little baby,
you were in my thoughts
before you did even exist

Babies are
made in heaven

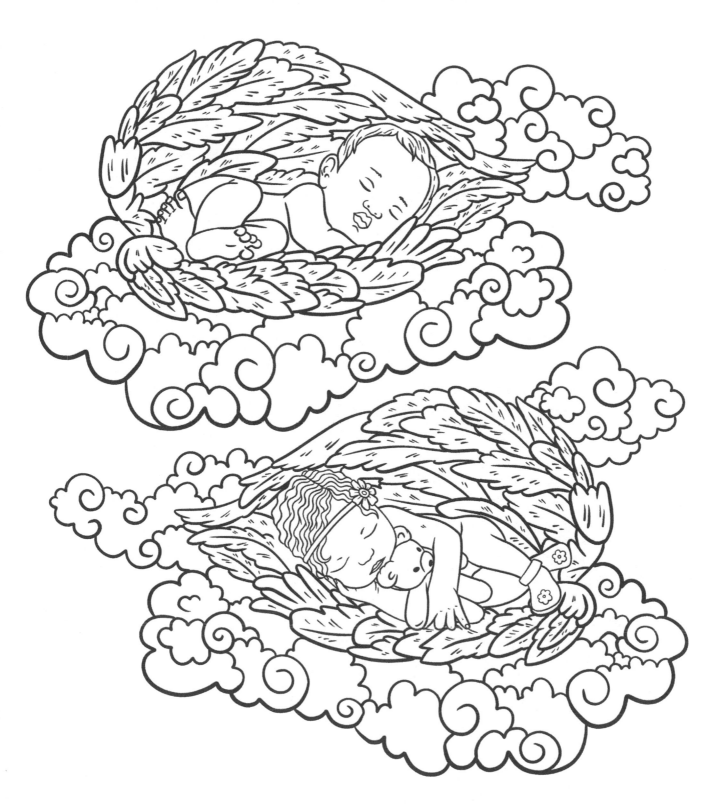

Dreams do come true

You are the only one who knows what my heart sounds like from the inside

I am ready for
a successful pregnancy

Every treatment takes me closer to my goal

Baby, your time to arrive is NOW

I accept help

My heart is fertile
My soul is fertile

Thank you
for the healthy baby

So be it

Thank you so much for coloring with Artrezor!

Check out our other coloring books, publications as well.

Made in the USA
Monee, IL
25 January 2023

26219148R00039